Going to School

Story by Neil Griffiths

D1685573

CITY OF LIME PUBLIC L

2

HAWTHORN CLOSE

PEDESTRIANS
push button and wait
for signal opposite

WAIT

wait   cross   do not start
        with care   to cross

FLASHING

POST OFFICE

Litter
SOFT DRINKS

OPEN

NEWS

72-page
property
guide

BITI

IN-STORE
NOW

6

CITY OF LIMERICK PUBLIC LIBRARY

TREDINGTON
PRIMARY
SCHOOL

CITY OF LIMERICK
PUBLIC LIBRARY